By

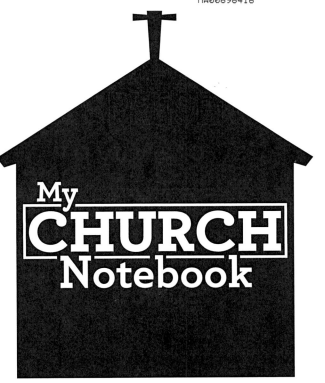

My CHURCH Notebook

COME INTO HIS PRESENCE

VOLUME ONE

This Church Notebook Belongs to:

_____

Truth:78

Acknowledgments

The following people have had an important part
in bringing this resource to publication.
With much appreciation for their efforts,
Truth78 anticipates with them
the eternal fruit of their labors.

Rachel Golias • design input
Karen Hieb • project management
Nicole Dunn Manuel • design and illustration

Truth:78 / Equipping the Next Generations
to Know, Honor and Treasure God

Truth78.org · info@Truth78.org · 877.400.1414 · @Truth78org

A Note to Children

Learning to sit in the church service can be a little hard to do. It is hard for kids to sit still for a long time, and at times you might get a little bored. But if you practice, and if you ask God to help you, it will get easier.

If you join in the singing, read along in your Bible when the Bible passage is being read, and listen carefully to the sermon, you will become more interested in the service. At first when you listen to the sermons, there will be things you don't understand. The pastor might use big words and thoughts that seem confusing to you. But as you listen carefully, little by little, you will understand more. As you pray and ask God for help, you will understand more of His Word, grow in your love for the truth, and begin seeing more of all that God is.

Little by little, you will learn about His greatness, His love, His holiness, His judgment, and His faithfulness. You will begin to know how He works in the world and what He has done in history for thousands of years. You will hear of His mighty acts and His loving heart for His people. You will learn why He should be feared and loved. You will begin to understand what Jesus did on the cross and why He did it. You will learn how much you need to depend on Jesus and how His death on the cross made a way for sinners to be saved. You will learn how to live in a way that is pleasing to Jesus and how the Holy Spirit can be your Helper.

As you worship among the people of God, remember that they are praying that you will you learn to love God with all your heart, mind, and soul, and that you will worship Him, giving thanks and praise and honor to Him in your heart.

So faith comes from hearing, and hearing through the word of Christ.

Romans 10:17

What does "COME INTO HIS PRESENCE" mean?

We are always in the presence of God. Another way to say this is that we are always with God. Psalm 139 tells us of this wonderful truth:

> *Where can I go from your Spirit? Or where shall I flee from your presence? [8]If I ascend to heaven, you are there! If I make my bed in Sheol, you are there! [9]If I take the wings of the morning and dwell in the uttermost parts of the sea, [10]even there your hand shall lead me, and your right hand shall hold me.*
> *—Psalm 139:7-10*

Because God is everywhere, all the time, we are never out of God's presence. God is always with us, and we are always with God.

But to "come into His presence" means more than just being with God. It is consciously thinking about being with God. It is concentrating on who God is, and thanking and praising Him for who He is. It is asking God what He has to say to us and what He wants us to do. It is recognizing that God is great, and that this great God has invited us to look upon His greatness.

We can do this alone—in our own rooms, with our own Bibles, and in our own hearts. Or we can consciously and deliberately come into God's presence with other people of God. Together, the people of God can help each other see the greatness of God, and praise Him for His greatness and goodness to us. Together we can ask Him to show us our sin, and then ask His forgiveness for offending Him, seeking to know Him better, and learning to trust Him more.

Sometimes other people can help us come into the presence of God. If your own heart is sad or worried about something, or even if you are distracted and having a hard time concentrating on God, sometimes if you see someone else singing praises to God, your own heart forgets its sadness or worry, and you remember the goodness of God. Seeing someone else praise God can help you to focus on praising God. Seeing the joy on someone else's face while that person is concentrating on God can sometimes help you come into the presence of God, too. This is one reason why we worship together.

This is what a Sunday morning church service is all about. It is about coming into the presence of God with other people of God. It is about concentrating on God.

But concentrating is sometimes hard! Our minds wander, and our hearts tug us away from God sometimes. This Church Notebook can help you to concentrate. It can help you come into the presence of God.

Before the Church Service Starts

PRAY that you will come into God's presence during the church service. Here are some things you can pray about:

- Ask God to show you something new about Himself this morning, or to help you understand Him better and love Him more.

- Ask God to soften your heart. Tell Him that you do not want to be stubborn before Him, but that you want to be an obedient child of His. Ask Him to give you a heart that loves the truth in the Bible and wants to obey His Word.

- Confess your sins to God. Ask Him to take away any sin that stands between you and Him.

- Ask God to help you to concentrate on Him during the church service. Tell him how easily you get distracted—how you can start thinking about the clothes the people are wearing or someone's new haircut—and ask Him to help you to focus on Him.

- Ask God to help you to understand His Word and to respond to His Word.

- Think about what God is like, and thank Him for being God.

Add your own ideas of what to pray about:

Other Things to Do Before the Church Service Starts

- Read the church bulletin.
- Read and think about the words of the hymns and worship songs. When it is time to sing these songs, think about the words and sing, not only with your mouth but with your heart. This means that if the song or hymn is about the greatness of God, sing with enthusiasm. If it is a quiet song to help you think about the worth of God, sing with a humble and sincere heart.
- Find the Bible passage for the sermon. Read and think about it, and ask God to show you something new in His Word. Put a bookmark in the place so you can find the passage quickly during the service. When the passage is read during the church service, follow the reading in your own Bible.
- Pray for others. Pray for the pastor and his family (and for other pastors and their families if your church has more than one pastor). Pray for the people leading the service. Pray for missionaries your church has sent out. Sometimes these people are listed in the bulletin. Pray for other people you know in the church. Pray for Christians in other countries. Pray for unsaved people you know and unsaved people in other countries.
- Write the sermon title and the Scripture passage for the morning in your Church Notebook.

Add your own ideas of what to do before the church service starts:

How to Use This Notebook

Fill in the **sermon title**, **preacher's name**, **Scripture passage**, and **date** before the church service starts.

 Listen for the most important things the preacher says—these are sometimes called **key points** or **main ideas**. Sometimes a pastor will list these for you by numbering them. Sometimes a preacher will talk a long time about one thought—this can be a main point. Sometimes you can tell the pastor's main point by how he speaks—sometimes a preacher will say main points more slowly or louder than other things. (These are not always main points, but they can be.) Write down the thoughts that seem most important to the preacher, and then think about these main points. Write these main points in the section with a **key** on your Church Notebook page.

 Sometimes, when we write about something **exciting** or something we think is **really important**, we put an exclamation point at the end of the sentence—like this! Sometimes, a preacher may say something that is exciting, new, or important to you. It may not be a main point, but it might be a main point for you—something you need to learn, hear, or obey—or maybe something new you learned about God or something that made you appreciate God more. Write these thoughts that are exciting, new, or important for you by the **exclamation points**.

 Often, something the preacher says makes a **question** pop into your mind. It might be something the sermon made you think about. It might be something the preacher said that you don't understand. It might be a word you don't know. It might be something that you are wondering about God. These are questions you can ask your parents about after

church—maybe when you eat lunch together or in the car on the way home. Write your questions by the **question marks.**

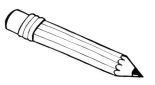

We can never understand God fully. He is so great, so complex (complicated), and so extraordinary that we are not able to understand all that there is about God. But we can understand many things about God, and we can learn to know who He is more personally. As you listen to the sermon or think about the Bible text, you might discover **something new about God,** or even just be reminded about what He is like. Write something you learned about God in the box with the **pencil.**

The Bible says that we should not just be "hearers" or the Word but we should be **"doers"** of the Word (James 1:22). This means that when we read the Bible or hear a sermon, we need to think about **what God wants us to think, be, or do** because of what we just read or heard. This might be:

- a sin in your life you need to repent of
- a command of God you need to obey (for example: "love one another")
- a bad habit God is asking you to change, or a new good habit He is asking you to start
- someone God puts on your heart to pray for
- an attitude of your heart that needs to change
- a wrong idea you have that needs to be corrected
- maybe you need to ask forgiveness from someone
- a praise for what God has done or what He is like
- a verse or thought you can use in encouraging someone else

There may be any number of ways God may be speaking to you. God wants us to act on His Word, not just hear it and then go home and forget about it. God wants us to change as a result of hearing His Word. So you need to ask God, "What do you want me to think, be, or do with what I heard from the preacher or read in the Bible today?" Talk with your mom or dad about how you can respond to God's Word. Pray about what God is asking you to think, be, or do. You might know the answer immediately, or maybe it will be a day or two later. But don't just forget about what you read or heard. When you know the answer, **write it in the section with the hands, feet, or heart images on your page.** Then do what God is asking you to do. Be a "doer" of the Word, not just a "hearer."

A Note for Parents:
Suggestions for Helping Your Child Worship

Sometimes, the difference for children between enduring Sunday morning services and enjoying Sunday morning services is simply a matter of preparation and training. It is my heartfelt prayer that your child will come as a participant in the service to worship our great God. To that end, I have prepared a few suggestions that might help you lead your child to worship this morning.

1. **Be prepared for worship.**

    Sunday morning starts Saturday night—lay out clothes (find all shoes!), get offerings ready, rehearse memory verses, gather together everything you need to bring with you, etc. before Sunday morning.

    Keep Sunday simple—make a simple breakfast and leave the house with time to spare.

    Remind your child of your expectations of his behavior during the church service.

2. **Be a role model for your child.**

    Start your morning with a positive attitude, a cheerful tone, a spirit of anticipation and enthusiasm, and a heart for worship.

3. **Walk your child through the service before it starts.**

    Arrive early and look over the bulletin; point out what will be happening and how your child can participate. This may mean teaching him a refrain of a responsive reading or teaching him a phrase from a song or worship song and asking him to listen for it.

    You may want to pray with your child before the service starts.

4. Encourage your child to participate in the service.

See if you can get a list of Sunday's songs in advance and listen to them at home during the week before. By teaching your child hymns and worship songs at home, he will be able to participate in the service. If he cannot learn the whole hymn, teach the refrain and signal to him when it is time to sing the part he knows. Encourage your child to sit and to stand at the appropriate times, to clap when appropriate, etc. If a hymn book is used, show him the words in the hymn book, moving your finger along as the hymn is sung. (Even if your child is a non-reader, this will help to focus his attention and encourage him to pay attention to the words.) Have your child bring an offering and place it in the plate.

5. Help your child become an active sermon listener.

When necessary, help your child to focus on the sermon by quietly whispering instructions to him, such as "Listen to this story" or "Can you draw a picture of...?" This is not a time of long instruction, but just very short statements to focus your child's attention. It is also not a time for your child to whisper back to you.

Encourage a younger child to listen to the sermon and to draw a picture of something from the sermon. (This should not be seen as a time for doodling, but for active listening.) If your child is very young and finds it difficult to sit still for a long time, after he has listened to the sermon for awhile, you may want to let him look at small Bible storybooks.

As your child gets older and learns to write, model for him how to take simple notes. Let him copy your notes at first; then encourage him to take his own. Read the introductory pages of this Church Notebook and discuss them with your child. Help your child use the Notebook effectively.

6. Stretch your child's ability to sit still and be attentive.

If you have a very young and active child, you may need to take your child out of the service part way through. Keep stretching him until he can sit through the whole service. You may need to be firm. Reaffirm positive behavior.

7. Talk about the service on the way home.

Speak positively with your child about the service, and ask him if he has any questions. Encourage him to share his drawings or notes.

To help you **LISTEN** and **PARTICIPATE**
so you can learn to **LOVE** and **WORSHIP GOD**...

Sermon Title: _____

Preacher's Name: _____ Date: _____

Scripture: _____

KEY POINTS:

_____

_____

_____

_____

_____

_____

NEW, **EXCITING** or **IMPORTANT** thoughts for me:

QUESTIONS I have:

WORDS I didn't understand:

Something I **LEARNED** about **GOD**:

What is **GOD** asking me to **DO**, **THINK**, **BE**?

Draw a picture of something you saw or heard in the service.

Space for additional notes and drawings:

Sermon Title: _____

Preacher's Name: _____ Date: _____

Scripture: _____

KEY POINTS:

_____

_____

_____

_____

_____

_____

NEW, **EXCITING** or **IMPORTANT** thoughts for me:

QUESTIONS I have:

WORDS I didn't understand:

Something I **LEARNED** about **GOD**:

What is **GOD** asking me to **DO**, **THINK**, **BE**?

Draw a picture of something you saw or heard in the service.

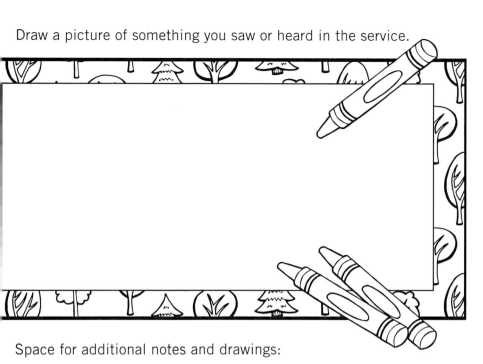

Space for additional notes and drawings:

To help you **LISTEN** and **PARTICIPATE**
so you can learn to **LOVE** and **WORSHIP GOD**...

Sermon Title:

Preacher's Name: _____ Date:

Scripture:

KEY POINTS:

NEW, **EXCITING** or **IMPORTANT** thoughts for me:

QUESTIONS I have:

WORDS I didn't understand:

Something I **LEARNED** about **GOD**:

What is **GOD** asking me to **DO, THINK, BE**?

Draw a picture of something you saw or heard in the service.

Space for additional notes and drawings:

To help you **LISTEN** and **PARTICIPATE**
so you can learn to **LOVE** and **WORSHIP GOD**...

Sermon Title:

Preacher's Name: Date:

Scripture:

KEY POINTS:

NEW, **EXCITING** or **IMPORTANT** thoughts for me:

QUESTIONS I have:

WORDS I didn't understand:

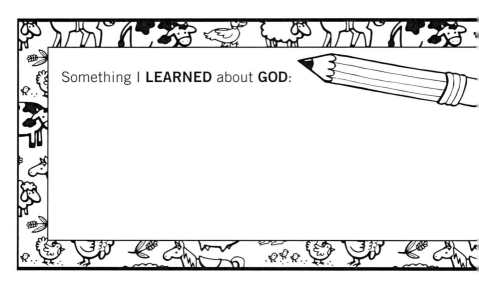

Something I **LEARNED** about **GOD**:

What is **GOD** asking me to **DO**, **THINK**, **BE**?

Draw a picture of something you saw or heard in the service.

Space for additional notes and drawings:

To help you **LISTEN** and **PARTICIPATE**
so you can learn to **LOVE** and **WORSHIP GOD**...

Sermon Title: _____

Preacher's Name: _____ Date: _____

Scripture: _____

KEY POINTS:

_____

_____

_____

_____

_____

_____

NEW, **EXCITING** or **IMPORTANT** thoughts for me:

QUESTIONS I have:

WORDS I didn't understand:

Something I **LEARNED** about **GOD**:

What is **GOD** asking me to **DO**, **THINK**, **BE**?

Draw a picture of something you saw or heard in the service.

Space for additional notes and drawings:

To help you **LISTEN** and **PARTICIPATE**
so you can learn to **LOVE** and **WORSHIP GOD**...

Sermon Title:

Preacher's Name: Date:

Scripture:

KEY POINTS:

NEW, **EXCITING** or **IMPORTANT** thoughts for me:

QUESTIONS I have:

WORDS I didn't understand:

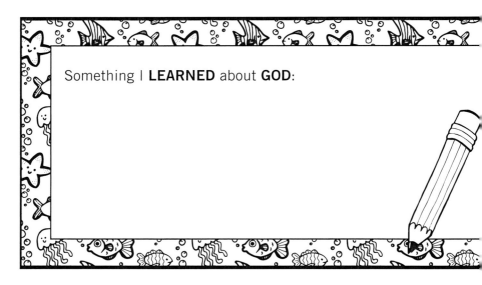

Something I **LEARNED** about **GOD**:

What is **GOD** asking me to **DO**, **THINK**, **BE**?

Draw a picture of something you saw or heard in the service.

Space for additional notes and drawings:

To help you **LISTEN** and **PARTICIPATE**
so you can learn to **LOVE** and **WORSHIP GOD**...

Sermon Title: _____

Preacher's Name: _____ Date: _____

Scripture: _____

KEY POINTS:

_____

_____

_____

_____

_____

_____

NEW, **EXCITING** or **IMPORTANT** thoughts for me:

QUESTIONS I have:

WORDS I didn't understand:

Something I **LEARNED** about **GOD**:

What is **GOD** asking me to **DO**, **THINK**, **BE**?

Draw a picture of something you saw or heard in the service.

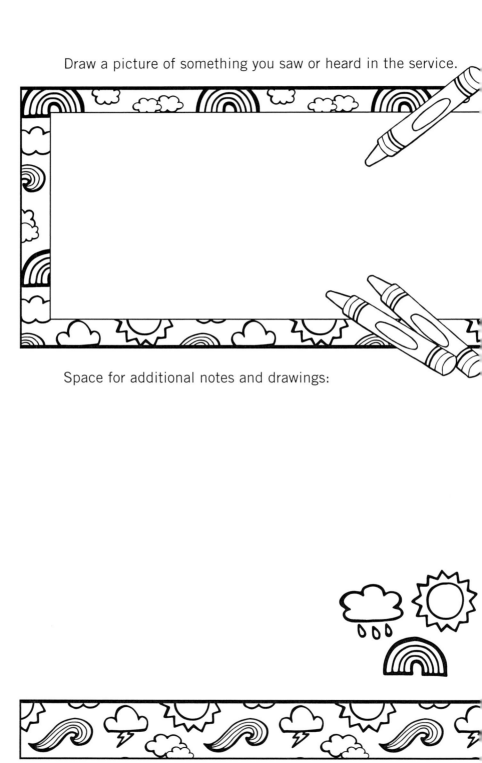

Space for additional notes and drawings:

To help you **LISTEN** and **PARTICIPATE**
so you can learn to **LOVE** and **WORSHIP GOD**...

Sermon Title:_____

Preacher's Name:_____ Date:_____

Scripture:_____

KEY POINTS:

_____

_____

_____

_____

_____

_____

NEW, **EXCITING** or **IMPORTANT** thoughts for me:

QUESTIONS I have:

WORDS I didn't understand:

Something I **LEARNED** about **GOD**:

What is **GOD** asking me to **DO**, **THINK**, **BE**?

Draw a picture of something you saw or heard in the service.

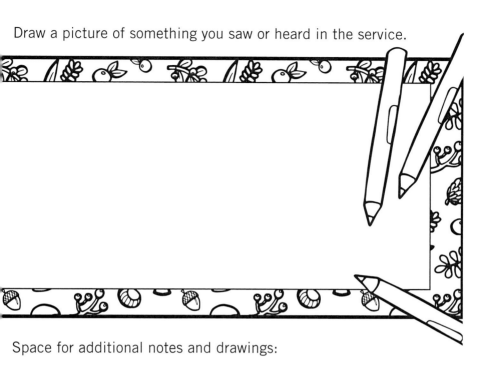

Space for additional notes and drawings:

To help you **LISTEN** and **PARTICIPATE**
so you can learn to **LOVE** and **WORSHIP GOD**...

Sermon Title:

Preacher's Name: _____ Date: _____

Scripture:

KEY POINTS:

_____

_____

_____

_____

_____

_____

NEW, **EXCITING** or **IMPORTANT** thoughts for me:

QUESTIONS I have:

WORDS I didn't understand:

Something I **LEARNED** about **GOD**:

What is **GOD** asking me to **DO**, **THINK**, **BE**?

Draw a picture of something you saw or heard in the service.

Space for additional notes and drawings:

To help you **LISTEN** and **PARTICIPATE**
so you can learn to **LOVE** and **WORSHIP GOD**...

Sermon Title: _____

Preacher's Name: _____ Date: _____

Scripture: _____

KEY POINTS:

_____

_____

_____

_____

_____

_____

NEW, **EXCITING** or **IMPORTANT** thoughts for me:

QUESTIONS I have:

WORDS I didn't understand:

Something I **LEARNED** about **GOD**:

What is **GOD** asking me to **DO**, **THINK**, **BE**?

Draw a picture of something you saw or heard in the service.

Space for additional notes and drawings:

To help you **LISTEN** and **PARTICIPATE**
so you can learn to **LOVE** and **WORSHIP GOD**...

Sermon Title:

Preacher's Name: Date:

Scripture:

KEY POINTS:

NEW, **EXCITING** or **IMPORTANT** thoughts for me:

QUESTIONS I have:

WORDS I didn't understand:

Something I **LEARNED** about **GOD**:

What is **GOD** asking me to **DO, THINK, BE**?

Draw a picture of something you saw or heard in the service.

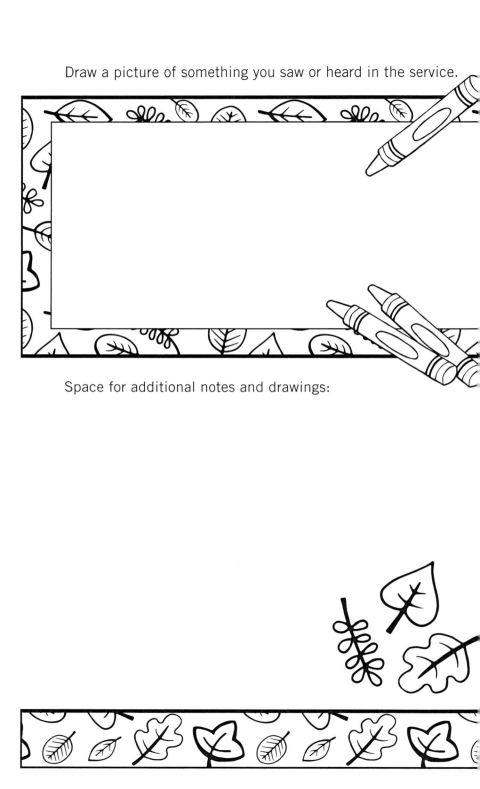

Space for additional notes and drawings:

To help you **LISTEN** and **PARTICIPATE**
so you can learn to **LOVE** and **WORSHIP GOD**...

Sermon Title:

Preacher's Name: _____ Date:

Scripture:

KEY POINTS:

NEW, **EXCITING** or **IMPORTANT** thoughts for me:

QUESTIONS I have:

WORDS I didn't understand:

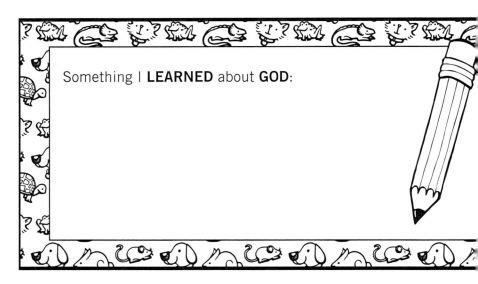

Something I **LEARNED** about **GOD**:

What is **GOD** asking me to **DO, THINK, BE**?

Draw a picture of something you saw or heard in the service.

Space for additional notes and drawings:

Sermon Title:

Preacher's Name: Date:

Scripture:

KEY POINTS:

NEW, **EXCITING** or **IMPORTANT** thoughts for me:

QUESTIONS I have:

WORDS I didn't understand:

Something I **LEARNED** about **GOD**:

What is **GOD** asking me to **DO**, **THINK**, **BE**?

Draw a picture of something you saw or heard in the service.

Space for additional notes and drawings:

Sermon Title:

Preacher's Name: Date:

Scripture:

KEY POINTS:

NEW, **EXCITING** or **IMPORTANT** thoughts for me:

QUESTIONS I have:

WORDS I didn't understand:

Something I **LEARNED** about **GOD**:

What is **GOD** asking me to **DO**, **THINK**, **BE**?

Draw a picture of something you saw or heard in the service.

Space for additional notes and drawings:

To help you **LISTEN** and **PARTICIPATE**
so you can learn to **LOVE** and **WORSHIP GOD**...

Sermon Title: _____

Preacher's Name: _____ Date: _____

Scripture: _____

KEY POINTS:

_____

_____

_____

_____

_____

_____

NEW, **EXCITING** or **IMPORTANT** thoughts for me:

QUESTIONS I have:

WORDS I didn't understand:

Something I **LEARNED** about **GOD**:

What is **GOD** asking me to **DO**, **THINK**, **BE**?

Draw a picture of something you saw or heard in the service.

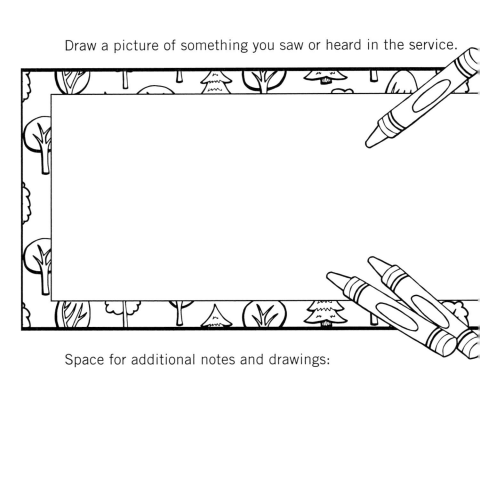

Space for additional notes and drawings:

Sermon Title:

Preacher's Name: Date:

Scripture:

KEY POINTS:

NEW, **EXCITING** or **IMPORTANT** thoughts for me:

QUESTIONS I have:

WORDS I didn't understand:

Something I **LEARNED** about **GOD**:

What is **GOD** asking me to **DO**, **THINK**, **BE**?

Draw a picture of something you saw or heard in the service.

Space for additional notes and drawings:

To help you **LISTEN** and **PARTICIPATE**
so you can learn to **LOVE** and **WORSHIP GOD**...

Sermon Title:

Preacher's Name: Date:

Scripture:

KEY POINTS:

NEW, **EXCITING** or **IMPORTANT** thoughts for me:

QUESTIONS I have:

WORDS I didn't understand:

Something I **LEARNED** about **GOD**:

What is **GOD** asking me to **DO**, **THINK**, **BE**?

Draw a picture of something you saw or heard in the service.

Space for additional notes and drawings:

To help you **LISTEN** and **PARTICIPATE** so you can learn to **LOVE** and **WORSHIP GOD**...

Sermon Title:

Preacher's Name: Date:

Scripture:

KEY POINTS:

NEW, **EXCITING** or **IMPORTANT** thoughts for me:

QUESTIONS I have:

WORDS I didn't understand:

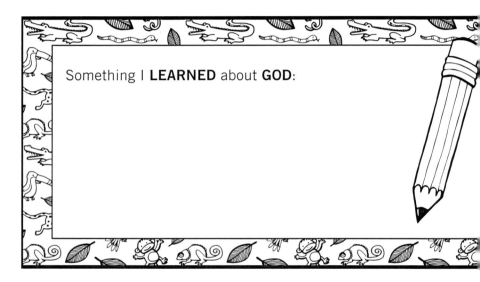

Something I **LEARNED** about **GOD**:

What is **GOD** asking me to **DO**, **THINK**, **BE**?

Draw a picture of something you saw or heard in the service.

Space for additional notes and drawings:

Sermon Title:_____

Preacher's Name:_____ Date:_____

Scripture:_____

KEY POINTS:

_____

_____

_____

_____

_____

_____

NEW, **EXCITING** or **IMPORTANT** thoughts for me:

QUESTIONS I have:

WORDS I didn't understand:

Something I **LEARNED** about **GOD**:

What is **GOD** asking me to **DO**, **THINK**, **BE**?

Draw a picture of something you saw or heard in the service.

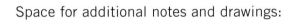

Space for additional notes and drawings:

Sermon Title: _____

Preacher's Name: _____ Date: _____

Scripture: _____

KEY POINTS:

_____

_____

_____

_____

_____

_____

NEW, **EXCITING** or **IMPORTANT** thoughts for me:

QUESTIONS I have:

WORDS I didn't understand:

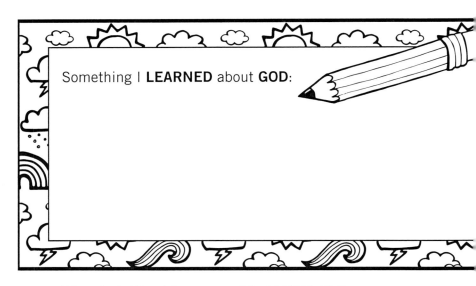

Something I **LEARNED** about **GOD**:

What is **GOD** asking me to **DO**, **THINK**, **BE**?

Draw a picture of something you saw or heard in the service.

Space for additional notes and drawings:

To help you **LISTEN** and **PARTICIPATE**
so you can learn to **LOVE** and **WORSHIP GOD**...

Sermon Title:_____

Preacher's Name:_____ Date:_____

Scripture:_____

KEY POINTS:

_____

_____

_____

_____

_____

_____

NEW, **EXCITING** or **IMPORTANT** thoughts for me:

QUESTIONS I have:

WORDS I didn't understand:

Something I **LEARNED** about **GOD**:

What is **GOD** asking me to **DO, THINK, BE**?

Draw a picture of something you saw or heard in the service.

Space for additional notes and drawings:

To help you **LISTEN** and **PARTICIPATE**
so you can learn to **LOVE** and **WORSHIP GOD**...

Sermon Title: _____

Preacher's Name: _____ Date: _____

Scripture: _____

KEY POINTS:

_____

_____

_____

_____

_____

_____

NEW, **EXCITING** or **IMPORTANT** thoughts for me:

QUESTIONS I have:

WORDS I didn't understand:

Something I **LEARNED** about **GOD**:

What is **GOD** asking me to **DO**, **THINK**, **BE**?

Draw a picture of something you saw or heard in the service.

Space for additional notes and drawings:

To help you **LISTEN** and **PARTICIPATE**
so you can learn to **LOVE** and **WORSHIP GOD**...

Sermon Title: _____

Preacher's Name: _____ Date: _____

Scripture: _____

KEY POINTS:

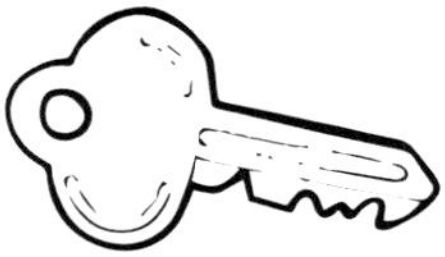

_____

_____

_____

_____

_____

_____

NEW, **EXCITING** or **IMPORTANT** thoughts for me:

QUESTIONS I have:

WORDS I didn't understand:

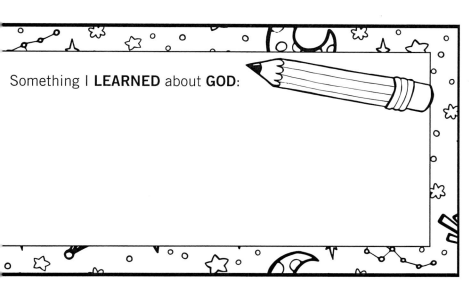

Something I **LEARNED** about **GOD**:

What is **GOD** asking me to **DO, THINK, BE**?

Draw a picture of something you saw or heard in the service.

Space for additional notes and drawings:

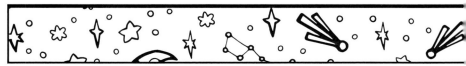

To help you **LISTEN** and **PARTICIPATE**
so you can learn to **LOVE** and **WORSHIP GOD**...

Sermon Title: _____

Preacher's Name: _____ Date: _____

Scripture: _____

KEY POINTS:

_____

_____

_____

_____

_____

_____

NEW, **EXCITING** or **IMPORTANT** thoughts for me:

QUESTIONS I have:

WORDS I didn't understand:

Something I **LEARNED** about **GOD**:

What is **GOD** asking me to **DO**, **THINK**, **BE**?

Draw a picture of something you saw or heard in the service.

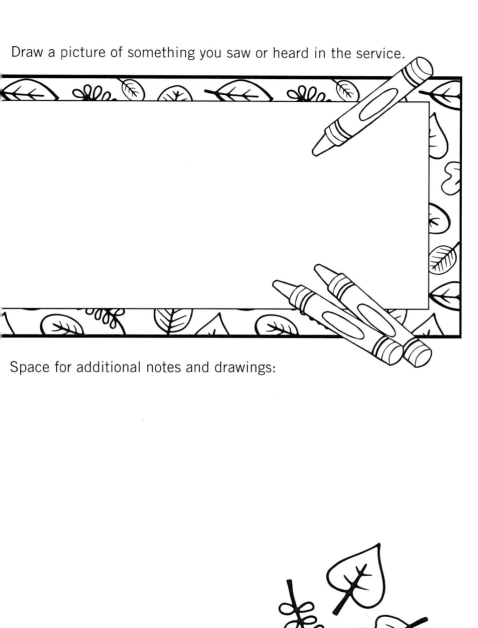

Space for additional notes and drawings:

Sermon Title:

Preacher's Name: _____ Date:

Scripture:

KEY POINTS:

NEW, **EXCITING** or **IMPORTANT** thoughts for me:

QUESTIONS I have:

WORDS I didn't understand:

Something I **LEARNED** about **GOD**:

What is **GOD** asking me to **DO**, **THINK**, **BE**?

Draw a picture of something you saw or heard in the service.

Space for additional notes and drawings:

Sermon Title:

Preacher's Name: Date:

Scripture:

KEY POINTS:

NEW, **EXCITING** or **IMPORTANT** thoughts for me:

QUESTIONS I have:

WORDS I didn't understand:

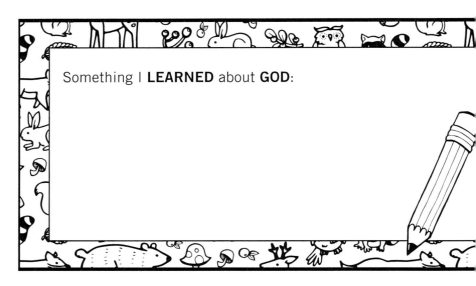

Something I **LEARNED** about **GOD**:

What is **GOD** asking me to **DO**, **THINK**, **BE**?

Draw a picture of something you saw or heard in the service.

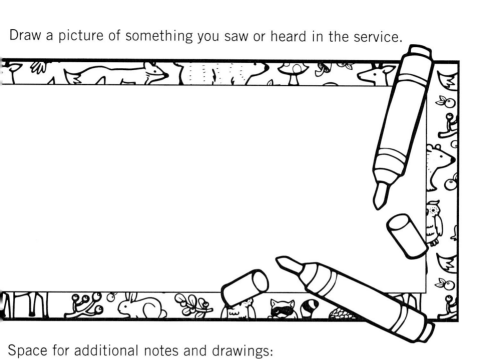

Space for additional notes and drawings:

Truth:78

Truth78 is a vision-oriented ministry for the next generations—that they may know, honor, and treasure God, setting their hope in Christ alone, so that they will live as faithful disciples for the glory of God.

Our mission is to nurture the faith of the next generations by equipping the church and home with resources and training that instruct the mind, engage the heart, and influence the will through proclaiming the whole counsel of God.

We are committed to developing resources and training that are God-centered, Bible-saturated, Gospel-focused, Christ-exalting, Spirit-dependent, doctrinally grounded, discipleship-oriented.

RESOURCES AND TRAINING MATERIALS

Truth78 currently offers the following categories of resources and training materials:

VISION-CASTING AND TRAINING

We offer a wide variety of booklets, video and audio seminars, articles, and other practical training resources that highlight and further expound our vision, mission, and values, as well as our educational philosophy and methodology. Many of these resources are freely distributed through our website. These resources and trainings serve to assist ministry leaders, volunteers, and parents in implementing Truth78's vision and mission in their churches and homes.

CURRICULUM

We publish materials designed for formal Bible instruction. The scope and sequence of these materials reflects our commitment to teach children and youth the whole counsel of God over the course of their education. Materials include curricula for Sunday School, Midweek Bible programs, Backyard Bible Clubs or Vacation Bible School, and Intergenerational studies. Most of these materials can be adapted for use in Christian schools and education in the home.

PARENTING AND FAMILY DISCIPLESHIP

We have produced a variety of materials and training resources designed to help parents disciple their children. These include booklets, video presentations, family devotionals, children's books, articles, and other recommended resources. Furthermore, our curricula include Growing in Faith Together (GIFT) Pages to help parents apply what is taught in the classroom to their child's daily experience in order to nurture faith.

BIBLE MEMORY

Our Fighter Verses Bible memory program is designed to encourage churches, families and individuals in the lifelong practice and love of Bible memory. The Fighter Verses program utilizes an easy-to-use Bible memory system with carefully chosen verses to help fight the fight of faith. For pre-readers, Foundation Verses features 76 key verses with simple images. Visit FighterVerses.com for weekly devotionals and free memory aids. Download the Fighter Verses App for quizzes, songs, devotionals, review reminders, and other helps.

For more information on any of these resources and training materials contact:

Truth78.org · info@Truth78.org · 877.400.1414 · @Truth78org